Developing History

UNDERSTANDING AND INTERPRETING THE PAST

Ages 6-7

Anita Loughrey

A & C BLACK

Contents

How do we know about the Great Fire of London?

How do we know about the Ancient Greek Olympic Games?

Remembrance Day

Published 2007 by A & C Black Publishers Limited
38 Soho Square, London W1D 3HB
www.acblack.com

ISBN 978-0-7136-8392-9

Copyright text and illustrations © Bender Richardson White
Copyright cover illustration © Sholto Walker
Copyright photo on page 17 © Topham Picturepoint
Project managers: Lionel Bender and Ben White
Editors: Lucy Poddington and Deborah Kespert
Design: Susan McIntyre
Illustrator: Gaynor Berry

The publishers would like to thank Rick Weights and Alf
Wilkinson of the Historical Association for their assistance in
producing this series of books.

A CIP catalogue record for this book is available from the
British Library.

Printed in Great Britain by Martins the Printers, Berwick
on Tweed

This book is produced using paper that is made from wood
grown in managed, sustainable forests. It is natural, renewable
and recyclable. The logging and manufacturing processes
conform to the environmental regulations of the country
of origin.

Introduction

Developing History is a series of seven photocopiable activity books for history lessons. Each book provides a range of activities that not only develop children's knowledge and understanding of events, people and changes in the past, but also provide opportunities to develop their investigative and interpretive skills.

The activities vary in their approach. Some are based on first-hand observations, some present text and images for the children to analyse, and others require the children to find information from books and electronic sources. They focus on questioning, observing, generating thoughts and ideas, planning, carrying out investigations, recording findings, checking and questioning findings and presenting explanations. The activities include independent and group work.

The activities in **Ages 6–7** are based on the QCA schemes of work for history at Key Stage 1 and support children's development in the following areas from the programme of study:

- Place events and objects in chronological order
- Use common words and phrases relating to the passing of time
- Recognise why people did things, why events happened and what happened as a result
- Identify differences between ways of life at different times
- Identify different ways in which the past is represented
- Find out about the past from a range of sources of information
- Ask and answer questions about the past
- Communicate in a variety of ways.

The activities are linked with other areas of the curriculum where appropriate.

Each activity specifies the learning outcome and features a **Teachers' note** at the foot of the page, which may be masked before photocopying. This will flag any resources needed for the activity. Expanded teaching notes are also provided in the **Notes on the activities** on pages 5–11. This section gives further information and provides key vocabulary to work through at the start of each activity.

Most of the activity sheets end with a challenge (**Now try this!**) which reinforces and extends the children's learning and provides the teacher with an opportunity for assessment. These activities might be appropriate for only a few children; it is not expected that the whole class should complete them. A separate sheet of paper will be needed for some of the extension activities.

Most children will be able to carry out the activities independently. It is not expected that the children will be able to read all the instructions on the sheets, but that someone will read with them. Children gradually become accustomed to seeing instructions, and learn their purpose long before they can read them.

Organisation and resources

Most activities require few resources beyond pencils and general classroom items, including spare paper on occasion. To give all children the best opportunity for developing effectively their knowledge and understanding of the world the children will need opportunities to gather information and satisfy their curiosity. They will begin to understand the past by examining appropriate artefacts (such as toys played with by their parents when they were young), looking at books, using CD-ROMs, audio and visual reference material, pictures, photographs, maps and by talking to visitors and making visits. Consequently, there will be times when children will need additional resources to complete the activities. These will be pointed out in the **Teachers' note**. It would also be useful to have a chart on the wall listing months and days.

You may want to use electronic interactive whiteboards or overhead projectors to display activity sheets or source material. You will also find it helpful to build up your own resource bank of books, posters, newspapers and old photographs, especially of your local area or historic sites you and your class have visited.

Structure of a history lesson

To get the best use of the activity sheets, gather all the resources you need before the lesson. Spend 10–15 minutes discussing the activity and making sure all the children understand what they have to do and how they will achieve it. Give the children about 20 minutes on the activity. Allow 5–10 minutes for whole-class review and consolidation.

Useful websites

You can find information and pictures relating to the topics in this book on the following websites:
www.actilingua.com/AboutVienna/composers/mozart.php

www.britishbattles.com/crimean-war/balaclava.htm

www.victorianweb.org

www.buildingsoflondon.co.uk

www.ancient-greece.co.uk

www.olympic.org

www.britishlegion.org.uk

www.florence-nightingale.co.uk

www.maryseacole.com

Further references to useful online resources are included in the **Notes on the activities** on pages 5–11.

Notes on the activities

The notes below expand upon those provided at the foot of the activity pages. They give ideas for making the most of the activity sheet, including suggestions for the whole-class introduction and discussion or for follow-up work using an adapted version of the sheet. To help teachers to select appropriate learning experiences for their pupils, the activities are grouped into sections within each book, but the pages need not be presented in the order in which they appear unless stated otherwise.

Looking at historical evidence

Finding out (page 12) explores different ways people find out about the past. Explain that we know what has happened in the past because information has been collected and recorded. Historians use this evidence to find out how people used to live. You could use this activity sheet for draft work to be written up in neat in a Word document. If possible scan in photos and drawings to support their writing and print off for display. This sheet links to objectives in citizenship (Taking part).

> **Vocabulary:** *when, event, information, historian.*

Evidence about me (page 13) focuses on how we discover the past. Explain that the children are going to record personal information that might be useful for a future historian. Organise a class time capsule to be buried in the school grounds. Ask what sort of things should go in it to show what school is like today. Encourage them to justify why their suggested item should be included in the time capsule. This activity could be used to support work in science (Variation).

> **Vocabulary:** *record, evidence, information, historian.*

Secondary or primary? (page 14) encourages the children to identify primary and secondary sources. Explain that historians use a wide variety of sources to answer questions about the past. Arrange for someone to visit the school to talk about different types of evidence. Show primary sources and discuss what they tell us about the past. Primary sources include letters, manuscripts, diaries, journals, newspapers, speeches, interviews, memoirs, documents produced by government agencies, photographs, audio recordings, video recordings, research data, objects and artefacts such as paintings, buildings, jewellery and weapons. Secondary sources do not come from the time being studied but were created after. Have a selection of history books and encyclopaedias available for the children to explore. Set up a display showing different types of evidence. Link to geography (Investigating our local area).

> **Vocabulary:** *primary, secondary, sources, past, future, present.*

Archaeology (page 15) introduces another important form of historical evidence. Before the children start, let them take part in a mock dig in a school sand pit or designated area. Encourage them to record where each item was found using grids. Tell the children that the evidence archaeologists dig up can help build a picture of what it was like before photographs

and written evidence became available. It may be possible to borrow archaeologists' tools and photographs of local digs from your local museum service, or if a local college or university is conducting a dig it may be possible to be shown around. The activity meets the requirements for core learning in literacy (Listening and responding; Drama).

> **Vocabulary:** *archaeology, archaeologist, dig, tools, a long time ago, evidence.*

Written evidence (page 16) extends children's understanding of different types of written evidence used by historians. Explain that people can use old newspapers to find things out about events and people in the past. Newspapers list information on deaths, births and marriages, as well as telling people what happened in specific areas. This activity sheet could be used in conjunction with **Finding out** (page 12). The children could use the same event for their reports to emphasise the different ways of recording the same information. The activity can be used to support work in literacy (Understanding and interpreting texts; Creating and shaping texts).

> **Vocabulary:** *written evidence, newspapers, report, reporting.*

Photographic evidence (page 17) develops the children's awareness that to build up the bigger picture historians need to draw on more than one form of evidence. Have a selection of old photographs both black and white and sepia, and new colour photographs available for the children to look at. Encourage the children to point out the differences. Explain that observation is a very important skill for an historian. Put the photos in order, oldest first, using clues about the types of photos and from the pictures. This activity meets requirements of literacy (Group discussion and interaction).

> **Vocabulary:** *observation, photographic evidence.*

Timeline (page 18) focuses on ordering events. Before the children attempt the activity sheet arrange other things in chronological order like a selection of children in the class from oldest to youngest or photos of the local area. Use words associated with the passing of time. Encourage the children to find out when the Romans occupied Britain and add this to the timeline. This activity could be linked to work in mathematics (Measuring).

> **Vocabulary:** *chronological, before, after, old, older, oldest, first, second, century, decade.*

Museums (page 19) is designed to be used on a museum visit. Identify the wide range of sources in the exhibits. Adapt the sheet to support other history topics by specifying an area you would like the children to concentrate on such as the Victorians or transport. On return to school they could write up their sheets neatly for display and support with pictures and postcards of the exhibits. This activity sheet could be related to work in science (Grouping materials).

> **Vocabulary:** *museum, artefact, exhibit, now, then.*

What were seaside holidays like in the past?

Holiday calendar (page 20) encourages children to recall information about their holidays. Ask what types of activities they do? Where do they go? Do they visit seaside resorts? Find the places they have visited on maps and globes. If possible, use Google Earth and let the children zoom in on some of the popular seaside resorts they have visited. Identify the beach, the pier and the promenade. This activity supports geography (Going to the seaside) and can be linked to work in religious education (Celebrations).

> **Vocabulary:** *holiday, bank holiday, outing, resort.*

Spot the mistakes (page 21) draws attention to how seaside holidays have changed over the last 100 years. Show the children pictures and photographs of the seaside and ask what they can see. Explain that many piers were built during Victorian times to provide entertainment and amusements for tourists. Bathing machines were also a common feature at seaside resorts during Victorian times. Develop a seaside display of objects for the children to examine, such as shells, buckets and spades, bathing costumes, sunglasses, etc. The activity sheet meets the requirements of core learning in literacy (Group discussion and interaction) and geography (Going to the seaside).

> **Vocabulary:** *holiday, pier, promenade, bathing machine.*

Going for a swim (page 22) examines swimwear through the ages. Explain that one of the most noticeable things that has changed about seaside holidays is the clothing people wear. It is a fairly recent occurrence for people to take off most of their clothes on a beach. People would change in bathing machines. If they wanted to play on the sand they would keep all their clothes on. The activity supports literacy (Group discussion and interaction).

> **Vocabulary:** *swimsuit, recent, modern, old-fashioned.*

Holidays in the past (page 23) encourages children to identify appropriate questions to ask about holidays in the past. Teach the children traditional songs and rhymes about the seaside, such as *We do like to be Beside the Seaside, Bobby Shafto*, etc. Set up a role-play area of a souvenir shop or café. Find pictures of food eaten at the seaside, such as fish and chips, sticks of rock and ice cream. Explain how street sellers would walk along the beach and promenade selling their wares. This activity could be extended to link with ICT (Questions and answers).

> **Vocabulary:** *question, answer, seaside.*

Keepsakes (page 24) focuses on souvenirs and what they can tell us about seaside holidays in the past. We can find out about holidays in the past by talking to older people. Explain that Victorian times are beyond living memory. Clues like souvenirs, photos and buildings help us to know what it was like. Arrange for a parent/carer/grandparent to visit the class and tell the children about his or her childhood seaside holidays, using photographs, slides, artefacts and souvenirs to illustrate the story. Encourage the children to ask questions. Allow them to ask some of the questions they thought of for the **Holidays in the past** activity sheet. Discuss the answers the visitor gave. This activity supports core learning in literacy (Listening and responding) and geography (Going to the seaside).

> **Vocabulary:** *souvenir, memento, keepsake, reminder.*

Fun at the seaside (page 25) reinforces the idea that some things change whilst others stay the same. Set up a role-play area for children to act out their own seaside stories both modern and from times gone by. Encourage the children to pretend they are in Victorian times. What sort of activities would they enjoy doing? Let the children study and talk about the pictures on the activity sheet with a partner. Ask them to mime a seaside activity to the class for the others to guess. This activity matches core learning in literacy (Drama) and geography (Going to the seaside).

> **Vocabulary:** *past, present, both, similar, different.*

Investigating famous people from the past

What makes people famous? (page 26) prompts children to think what the word 'famous' means. Who do they know who is famous? Why is he or she famous? What other famous people from the past do they know about? What did they do to become famous? Children could hot-seat different famous people from the selection of pictures and others have to guess who they are by asking yes and no questions. This activity meets the requirements of literacy (Group discussion and interaction).

> **Vocabulary:** *famous, well-known, celebrity, star.*

Wolfgang Amadeus Mozart (page 27) identifies the main events of Mozart's story. Tell the children they are going to find out about a famous person who lived long ago, before even their parents, carers and grandparents were alive. Explain that Mozart (1756–91) was important because he achieved so much whilst he was still a child. When he was three years old he could play the piano. When he was six he was touring Europe and even gave a concert for the Emperor of Austria. At the age of 8 he was writing his own symphonies and by the age of 13 he was a concert master. Enlarge the pictures onto A3 paper or project onto an interactive whiteboard. Look at the clothes he is wearing and compare them with the clothes children wear today. Identify similarities and differences. What is he doing? The activity meets core learning in literacy (Group discussion and interaction; Speaking).

> **Vocabulary:** *compose, symphony, concert master, sequence.*

Unbelievable talent (page 28) provides an opportunity for children to infer information from a written account of Mozart's life. Read the story to the class:

> Nobody could believe it was a little boy who had written the music Mozart performed in his tours around Europe. His talent was so unbelievable that he was taken to the archbishop's home and locked in a room with nothing but a bed, table, music paper, a quill and some ink. The archbishop wanted him to prove he was the composer of all this new music. Mozart enjoyed writing down all the tunes in his head. Whilst locked in the room he wrote pages and pages of music. When the archbishop unlocked the door he was

amazed to find lots of finished melodies. There was no doubt Mozart had written all the tunes he had performed. He was famous throughout Europe before he was 10.

Encourage the children to suggest what Mozart was like and list adjectives such as *genius, intelligent, clever*, etc. After they have completed the activity sheet they could cut out each section to make a zig-zag book of the story. Add a final page called, 'Why do we remember Mozart?' The activity meets the requirements for core learning in literacy (Listening and responding).

> **Vocabulary:** *recount, famous, talent, genius.*

Thank you for the music (page 29) allows children to gain an understanding that Mozart was a popular musician of his era. Listen to some of Mozart's music. There are excerpts available online: http://essentialsofmusic.com/composer/mozart.html, www.actilingua.com/AboutVienna/composers/mozart.php. Tell the children what the piece is called and when it was written. Explain that historians know what his music sounded like because he wrote the music down. Show the children examples of written music. Discuss the musical instruments used for Mozart's music and compare with instruments used today. This activity sheet could be used to support learning in music (Rain, rain, go away – Exploring timbre, tempo and dynamics).

> **Vocabulary:** *instruments, melody, compose, pop star.*

Anne Frank (page 30) provides opportunities to infer information from Anne Frank's diary. Anne Frank lived in Amsterdam, Holland during WW2. Show the children where Amsterdam is on maps and globes. Explain that Anne Frank (1929–44) and her family went into hiding in a secret annex in her father's office building because they were going to be sent to a concentration camp, which is like a large prison. Tell the children Margot was Anne's older sister and she was 16. A call-up notice is a demand they must go to a concentration camp. Anne Frank was 13 when she started her diary. Read other extracts from the diary to give the children a greater understanding of her life and childhood. This page supports core learning in literacy (Understanding and interpreting texts) and work in citizenship (Living in a diverse world).

> **Vocabulary:** *Amsterdam, Holland, annex, secret, concentration camp, diary, WW2, Jew.*

Going into hiding (page 31) gives children the opportunity to gather information from a picture. Explain that Anne Frank did not realise the enormous change to her life having to hide away would mean. The Franks shared the annex with another family and lived there for two years before they were found and captured. It is possible to take a virtual tour of the secret annex at: www.annefrank.org. Read the extract dated Saturday, 11 July 1942 in Anne Frank's diary to give the children an idea of Anne's first impressions of the secret annex. Discuss examples of unfair treatment in stories and other literature, such as Cinderella. Ask the children for examples of what they think is fair and unfair. This page supports core learning in literacy (Understanding and interpreting texts) and can be linked to work in citizenship (Living in a diverse world).

> **Vocabulary:** *secret annex, hideout, Jew, discrimination.*

Why is Anne Frank famous? (page 32) encourages the children to identify reasons why Anne Frank is remembered today. Explain that Anne Frank is famous not because she wrote her diary but because her father had her diary published after her death. Her diary is a very important form of historical evidence as it provides a first-hand account of what it was like to be a Jew in WW2, see: www.annefrankguide.net. Anne Frank Day is 12 June. The page supports core learning in literacy (Understanding and interpreting texts) and can be linked to work in citizenship (Living in a diverse world).

> **Vocabulary:** *diary, famous, historical evidence, primary source.*

Why do we remember Florence Nightingale and Mary Seacole?

The Crimean War (page 33) locates the site of a historical event on a map. Explain that Florence Nightingale was a nurse who looked after wounded soldiers during the Crimean War. Ask the children what war is. Discuss that the Crimean War happened a long time ago in Victorian times. Britain, France and the Ottoman Empire (Turkey) were fighting Russia who had invaded Turkish land. Look at maps and globes and find the British Isles, France, Turkey and Russia. Talk about the type of transport available. Explain that the British army left England by sea on 5 September 1854 and arrived at the Crimea on 14 September 1854. Florence Nightingale left London on 21 October 1854. First she travelled to Paris and across France to Marseilles. Then, from Marseilles, she went by sea to Constantinople in Turkey. She arrived on 4 November 1854. Use this activity to support geography (An island home) and literacy (Listening and responding).

> **Vocabulary:** *long time ago, Victorian, British Isles, Turkey, Crimea, map, globe.*

The Charge of the Light Brigade (page 34) studies a famous battle from the Crimean War. Explain that the picture is of the Battle of Balaclava (1854). The Charge of the Light Brigade caused a sensation throughout the world because British troops were ordered to charge against the Russians' much larger and stronger army. Nearly all the British soldiers were killed or injured. Alfred, Lord Tennyson, wrote a famous poem about it called 'The Charge of the Light Brigade'. The poem can be found at: www.britishbattles.com/crimean-war/balaclava.htm. There is also a good selection of pictures on this website. This matches core learning in literacy (Group discussion and interaction; Speaking).

> **Vocabulary:** *Crimean War, uniforms, weapons.*

The lady with the lamp (page 35) introduces Florence Nightingale and her role in the Crimean War. List what the children already know about Florence Nightingale. Tell them she was a famous nurse who lived a long time ago. Ask them what nurses do and why they think nurses wear a uniform. Look at pictures of modern-day nurses and compare the uniforms with those worn in the Crimea. Invite a nurse to come and talk to the class about what they do. Explain that at night Florence Nightingale would carry a lantern to the bedsides of the wounded when she checked on them. This is why the soldiers called her 'the lady with the lamp'. Florence and her nurses helped thousands of injured soldiers, see:

www.florence-nightingale.co.uk. This activity supports work in citizenship (People who help us).

> **Vocabulary:** *then, now, modern, past, old-fashioned, uniform, nurse.*

Florence Nightingale's story (page 36) recounts the main events in the life of a famous person. Read the story to the class:

> Florence Nightingale was born in Florence, Italy. Her parents did not want her to be a nurse as it was not considered a suitable profession for a well-educated woman. Sidney Herbert, the Minister at War, appointed Florence to oversee the introduction of female nurses into the military hospitals in Turkey. They had never had female nurses in military hospitals before. Florence insisted the hospitals were cleaned to prevent disease and infection. When the Crimean War ended she went back to England and wrote a book called *Notes on Nursing*. It has been translated into 11 languages and is still in print today. She established the Nightingale Training School for Nurses at St Thomas' Hospital in London. In recognition of her efforts, Queen Victoria awarded Florence the Royal Red Cross in 1883. Her hard work and dedication made nursing the respectable profession it is today.

The correct order is: 2, 1, 6, 4, 5, 3. Use the activity sheet to help children produce their own zigzag books with a picture and information about Florence Nightingale's life on each page. Give each page a title like a chapter in a book. Create a final page called, 'Why do we remember Florence Nightingale?' The activity relates to objectives in literacy (Listening and responding; Creating and shaping texts).

> **Vocabulary:** *disease, infection, hospital, nurse, campaign.*

An invitation (page 37) contains an abridged version of the letter from Sidney Herbert to Florence Nightingale. Tell the children there had never been female nurses at military hospitals before. When Florence arrived she was shocked at the conditions and lack of medical supplies. The surgeons were not happy for nurses to be there as they felt it was unseemly for women to be near the wounded soldiers. However, there were so many wounded, they soon realised they needed Florence's help. Design posters advertising for nurses to go to Scutari hospital. Role-play recruiting nurses. Hold interviews in groups of three with one child as Florence Nightingale, another as Sidney Herbert and another as a nurse being interviewed for a job at Scutari hospital. After the interview the children playing Florence and Sidney should decide whether or not they are going to employ the nurse. The page relates to objectives in literacy (Listening and responding; Drama).

> **Vocabulary:** *Scutari hospital, nurses, surgeons, interview.*

Scutari hospital (page 38) allows children to share their thoughts about hygiene in the hospital. Explain that Florence Nightingale began to change things and discuss the improvements she made. The children could write an imaginary letter back to Sidney Herbert describing the conditions she found when she arrived at Scutari hospital. Emphasise the necessity for cleanliness and how it relates to better health. Draw before and after pictures to emphasise the changes Florence Nightingale introduced. Make posters to promote cleanliness around the school, such as picking up litter and washing hands before they eat. This activity could be linked to work in science (Health and growth).

> **Vocabulary:** *hygiene, hygienic, clean, dirty, germs, health.*

Remembering Florence Nightingale (page 39) encourages the children to identify reasons why Florence Nightingale is remembered today. Ask what Florence Nightingale could say to Queen Victoria to persuade her to send aid for the British soldiers and nurses in the Crimea. What sorts of things would Queen Victoria want to know before she agreed? This activity links to work in literacy (Creating and shaping texts; Drama).

> **Vocabulary:** *nurse, hospital, campaign, hygiene.*

Mary Seacole (page 40) identifies another famous person who made a great contribution by helping soldiers in the Crimean War. Read the story to the class:

> Mary Jane Grant Seacole (1805–81) was born in Jamaica. Her mother was a nurse and her father a Scottish soldier. She wanted to help Florence Nightingale at the Scutari hospital but her offer was turned down. Mary Seacole was determined to go to the Crimea so travelled there at her own expense. She set up the British Hotel just outside Balaclava where the Charge of the Light Brigade took place. Her good work was reported in the newspapers in London. When she returned to England she was awarded two medals for bravery and a big celebration was held in her honour.

More information can be found at: www.maryseacole.com. The correct order for the captions is 2, 3, 1, 4. Identify Jamaica on maps and globes and look at how far it is from the British Isles and Turkey. Produce zig-zag books in the style of Florence Nightingale's story. This activity relates to objectives in literacy (Listening and responding; Creating and shaping texts) and with geography (An island home).

> **Vocabulary:** *a long time ago, Jamaica, Victorian, British Isles, Turkey, Crimea.*

Mary Seacole's story (page 41) looks at the reasons Mary Seacole wanted to go to the Crimea and why the War Office rejected her offer. This activity needs to be approached carefully. Tell the children she was told that no more nurses were needed. This was not true. Why do they think Sidney Herbert would have said such a thing? Ask the children to try and put themselves in the place of Mary Seacole, considering how they might react if this had happened to them. The children could role-play being interviewed by Sidney Herbert the war minister. They could also role-play being doctors, nurses and patients in Mary Seacole's British Hotel. The children can stick the cards on large sheets of paper and, in small groups, add speech bubbles to record what they think the different characters might have said to each other. The activity can be linked to work in citizenship (Living in a diverse world) and literacy (Drama).

> **Vocabulary:** *Mary Seacole, British Hotel, nurses, patients, fair, unfair.*

Newsflash (page 42) encourages children to recount episodes from stories about the past. In March 1856, the Crimean War suddenly ended. In 1857, Mary published a best-selling autobiography called 'Wonderful Adventures of Mrs Mary Seacole in Many Lands'. *Punch* magazine published articles about Mary and the good work she had done in the Crimea. A gala in honour of Mary Seacole was held over four nights between 27 and 30 July 1857 at the Royal Surrey Gardens, on the banks of the River Thames in London. Over 80,000 people attended. This activity supports core learning in literacy (Creating and shaping texts).

> **Vocabulary:** *newspaper, news, recount, story, autobiography.*

Compare and contrast (page 43) encourages the children to make comparisons between the lives of Mary Seacole and Florence Nightingale. Point out that their actions were unusual for women during the 19th century. In small groups, the children can record what they know about Florence and Mary on large sheets of paper as spider diagrams. Ask them to identify what happened before, during and after they went to the Crimea using the letters 'b', 'd' or 'a'. The information can then be used to complete the activity sheet. This meets the requirements of literacy (Group discussion and interaction).

> **Vocabulary:** *Mary Seacole, Florence Nightingale, kind, caring, patient, hard-working, before, during, after.*

How do we know about the Great Fire of London?

The Monument (page 44) provides a context for the story. Show the children a picture of central London today. Encourage them to work out the name of the city and show them pye Monument commemorating the Great Fire. Locate the date the Great Fire of London took place on a timeline. Create a class display, which includes a map and pictures of London, as a point of reference for the activities. Encourage the children to find out who designed the Monument. This activity could be linked to work in Art and design (Can buildings speak?).

> **Vocabulary:** *London, a long time ago, Great Fire, Monument, timeline, 1666.*

Portrait gallery (page 45) looks at Charles II, Samuel Pepys and Christopher Wren. Explain that they lived a very long time ago, in the mid-17th century, in the period known as 'the Stuarts'. Locate this on a simple timeline. Explain who Charles II was, introduce Samuel Pepys as someone who saw the fire and wrote about it and Christopher Wren as a citizen from the time who helped to rebuild London after the Great Fire. Look at how their clothes compare with modern-day clothes. The activity relates to objectives in literacy (Listening and responding).

> **Vocabulary:** *Charles II, Samuel Pepys, Christopher Wren, Stuarts, a very long time ago.*

Fire! Fire! (page 46) encourages the children to sequence events. If possible watch a video re-enactment of the Great Fire. Draw a line across the middle of large sheets of paper for the children to work on in pairs. Divide the line into quarters to symbolise the four days. Label from 2 September 1666 to 5 September 1666. Stick the events in order along this timeline. The correct order for the pictures is 5, 4, 2, 6, 3 and 1. The children could write fire poems using their senses and the

sentences they have written in the extension activity. This activity matches core learning in literacy (Group discussion and interaction).

> **Vocabulary:** *a very long time ago, began, first, next, then, after, at last, finally.*

When? Where? Why? (page 47) develops skills of reasoning. Discuss the reasons why the fire spread so rapidly and why people took refuge in churches and in boats on the river. In small groups the children could take on the role of someone at the fire, such as the baker in Pudding Lane, a ferry boat owner taking people across the Thames, someone whose house was pulled down to stop the fire's path and someone trying to put the fire out. Encourage them to think what they would have done if they were in the Great Fire. Would they have tried to escape? Would they have taken their belongings with them? Would they have stopped to help? This activity supports core learning in literacy (Speaking; Drama).

> **Vocabulary:** *because, reason, explanation, result, effect.*

London's burning (page 48) assesses the children's understanding. Tell the children the fire spread so quickly because it was very windy, the houses were very close together and it was the end of a very hot summer and the water wells were nearly dry. The only water available came from the River Thames. The first reaction was to run away. When they realised the fire was not going to go out on its own more people came to help. They created fire breaks by pulling down houses so the fire would not continue to spread. The Tower of London was saved in this way. On the third day the strong wind dropped and the fire eventually died down and stopped at Pye Corner. The activity relates to work in literacy (Listening and responding).

> **Vocabulary:** *flames, fire breaks, destroyed, saved.*

Samuel Pepys' diary (page 49) helps to gain an understanding of what an eyewitness is. Discuss how an eyewitness can help us to know what happened in the past. Show pictures of the Great Fire. Help the children recognise things an eyewitness would see, such as people in boats on the river, the direction of the fire's smoke. Discuss what a diary is and whether it is fact or fiction. Why are diaries important forms of evidence? Read extracts from Pepys' diary from: www.pepys.info. Explain that this is one man's personal account. Identify the things they already knew in the passage and the things they did not know. Identify facts and opinions opinions. More information can be found at www.pepysdiary.com. Explain that there are strengths and weaknesses in eyewitness accounts. There can be different representations of the same event. See also John Evelyn's and the Earl of Clarendon's diaries. This activity matches core learning in literacy (Group discussion and interaction).

> **Vocabulary:** *eyewitness, diary, first-hand, woodcut.*

Sir Christopher Wren (page 50) looks at the rebuilding of London and the work of Sir Christopher Wren. Tell the children that after the fire half the city had been destroyed and over 100,000 people were made homeless. Plans were made to rebuild the city and instead of narrow alleys of timber-framed, thatched houses they decided to build wide streets with buildings of bricks and stone. Sir Christopher Wren (1632–1723) was one of the main designers employed to do this. More information can be found out about him from: www.arct.cam.ac.uk/personal-page/james/phd/wren/date.html. The children could split into small groups to find out more about the buildings he designed. Produce leaflets to show what they found out. The page relates to literacy (Listening and responding).

> **Vocabulary:** *timber-framed, plaster, thatch, buildings, streets, rebuilt.*

St Paul's Cathedral (page 51) examines the history of an important historical building in London. St Paul's Cathedral was burned to the ground in the fire so a new cathedral was built to replace it. This was designed by Sir Christopher Wren, who submitted three different designs before they were finally approved. Rebuilding began in 1675 and was completed in 1710. Ask the children to explain the use of different spaces inside the cathedral, such as a space for entering and leaving, a space for the choir, a space for the congregation, etc. Ask them what they know about how the cathedral is used. More information can be found at www.stpauls.co.uk. This activity can be linked to work in art and design (Can buildings speak?).

> **Vocabulary:** *church, abbey, cathedral, rebuilt, Sir Christopher Wren.*

The fire brigade (page 52) looks at why cities are safer from great fires today. Ask the children who puts out fires today. Explain there was no fire brigade in 1666. There were a few volunteers who had horse-drawn fire carts. The only equipment carried on the cart was barrels of water, leather buckets, hand-squirts and hooks. Produce a timeline of the fire service for display within the classroom. Use pictures printed from the Internet to illustrate your timeline. Explain that the first fire brigade was introduced in 1824 in Edinburgh. A compulsory fire brigade was not introduced until 1938. More information can be found at: www.firebrigadehistory.netfirms.com/at_a_glimpse.html. www.london-fire.gov.uk/about_us/our_history/the_way_we_were.asp. Discuss school fire procedures. Tell the children people are much more safety conscious today and buildings are built with fire safety in mind, such as fire doors, fire exits, fire alarms, fire extinguishers, sprinklers, etc. Invite the local fire brigade to talk to the children about what they should do in the event of a fire. Link to citizenship (People who help us).

> **Vocabulary:** *fire brigade, firefighter, fire cart, fire engine, then, now, past, present day.*

How do we know about the Ancient Greek Olympic Games?

How do we know? (page 53) encourages the children to use historical sources and record their findings. There is more information on the website: www.perseus.tufts.edu/Olympics/. Find Greece on maps and globes and see where it is in relation to the UK. Point out Athens. Discuss the variety of evidence used to find out about the ancient Greeks such as buildings, pottery and statues. Have a selection of artefacts for the children to examine and discuss. It may be possible to borrow some from your local museum service. This activity meets requirements of literacy (Listening and responding) and mathematics (Measuring).

> **Vocabulary:** *stade, stadium, Olympic Games, ancient Greeks.*

Olympic events (page 54) helps children recognise different events from the ancient Olympic Games. Ask the children what sporting events they know about. Talk about athletics and the various field and track events. Ensure the children recognise all the events shown on the activity sheet. Explain how athletes train very hard to be selected to represent their country. If possible, organise your own Olympic Games and athletic events in a series of PE lessons. Experiment with different ways of travelling, throwing and jumping, increasing their awareness of speed and distance. Link to work in PE (Athletic activities).

> **Vocabulary:** *a very long time ago, ancient, recent, a short time ago.*

Ancient Olympia (page 55) gives the children an impression of what ancient Olympia was like. Tell the children the Olympic Games were a time when the different Greek cities met together to show how strong they were. They played an important part in their religious festivals. The gymnasium was used for javelin and discus, the hippodrome for horse and chariot racing, the palaestra for wrestling, boxing and jumping, the stadium was used for foot races and the Temple of Zeus was where the award ceremony took place. This activity meets the requirements of core learning for literacy (Listening and responding).

> **Vocabulary:** *stadium, gymnasium, palaestra, hippodrome, temple, buildings, structure, Zeus.*

Athletic events (page 56) allows children to discover how the Games have been adapted over the years. Encourage the children to research when each of the athletic competitions was introduced to the Olympic Games and mark on a timeline. Tell the children the pentathlon became an Olympic sport with the addition of wrestling in 708 BC. It included running, jumping, wrestling, discus and javelin and was considered the most important part of the Games. Explain that only men were originally allowed to complete in the ancient Greek Olympic Games. A good interactive website is: www.ancient-greece.co.uk/festivals/story/olympics.html. This activity could be matched to core learning in PE (Athletic activities).

> **Vocabulary:** *running, jumping, wrestling, discus, javelin, shooting, fencing, swimming, riding.*

Ancient and modern (page 57) encourages the children to compare the ancient and modern games looking for similarities and differences. Discuss with the children what they know about the Olympic Games. Why are the games held? Who takes part? How do they prepare for the games? What are the different events? What prizes do the winners receive? Who watches the games? List the questions on one large sheet of paper and the answers on another. This activity matches the requirements of core learning in literacy (Group discussion and interaction).

> **Vocabulary:** *ancient, modern, past, present, then, now.*

Olympic traditions (page 58) explores Olympic traditions in the opening ceremony and the Olympic Truce. The truce was established in ancient Greece in the 9th century BC. A truce is an agreement between all nations to stop fighting. People could travel in safety to the Olympic Games and return afterwards to their own countries. Today the Olympic Truce is symbolised by the dove of peace with the Olympic flame in the background. Tell the children a flame is carried from Olympia to light the Olympic torch in the stadium at the beginning of the games. Explain the games are opened by some form of entertainment from the hosting country and then all the competitors march around the arena. The Greeks always lead the procession and the host nation comes last. The rings on the Olympic flag represent each of the five continents and include at least one colour from the flag of every country taking part. One athlete is chosen to say the Olympic oath. More details can be found at: www.olympic.org/uk/games/ancient/index_uk.asp. This activity matches core learning for literacy (Listening and responding).

> **Vocabulary:** *truce, peace, flag, flame, torch, rings, procession, oath.*

Remembrance Day

Anniversaries (page 59) helps children to recognise that symbols represent commemorative events. Ask why the children think people wear poppies. Through discussion, establish that poppies are worn on and around 11 November, Remembrance Day. Ask what sorts of things we remember. Are there special people we remember? Why is it important to remember? Tell them we remember people as a sign of respect. Make connections with the other events on the activity sheet. In a plenary, explain we remember Guy Fawkes on Bonfire Night on 5 November, Jesus at Christmas on 25 December, Rama and Sita at Divali around Oct/Nov and Halloween is remembering important people in our own lives who have died. It takes place on All Saint's Day Eve, 31 October. This activity links with RE (Celebrations) and citizenship (Living in a diverse world).

> **Vocabulary:** *commemorate, remembrance, anniversary.*

War memorial (page 60) encourages the children to use historical sources in their own locality to find out information. Arrange a visit to a local war memorial. Before you go, check if any of the children will be able to trace their ancestors. If it is not possible to visit your local war memorial, find information about significant war memorials on the Internet to complete the activity sheet. Ask them when might the war memorial have been built? How could we find out? What do the symbols mean? Why is there a list of names? Why did people want to build a war memorial? Are there war memorials in other towns or villages? Explain that the origins of Remembrance Day lie in WWI (1914–18) and local war memorials usually list the names of soldiers killed in WWI and WW2. Connect to core learning in mathematics (Using and applying mathematics).

> **Vocabulary:** *tally, WWI, WW2, memorial.*

Remembrance Day fact file (page 61) highlights that commemorations are linked to specific events. Tell the children poppies are sold on Remembrance Day each year in memory of those who lost their lives in war, in particular the two great wars. Explain Read the poem *In Flanders Fields* by Lieutenant Colonel John McCrae. A copy can be found at: www.arlingtoncemetery.net/flanders.htm. The poem refers to the poppies that grew in the fields in Belgium where the fighting had taken place. Show pictures of these poppy fields. Find Belgium on maps and globes. Tell the children that this poem is a form of historical evidence because it is John McCrae's first-hand account of what he saw and experienced. Compose simple rhyming couplets about poppies. This activity meets the requirements of literacy (Listening and responding).

> **Vocabulary:** *symbol, commemorate, evidence, poppy.*

Armistice (page 62) looks at when WWI and Armistice Day occurred. Discuss how WWI relates in time to other famous events and famous people they have studied and how it relates to generations in their family. Explain briefly that the war lasted a long time and soldiers from countries all over the world fought in this war and many died. Soldiers saw the poppies growing in the battlefields and they came to represent both loss and hope. Explain how the armistice (ceasefire) to end the war happened on the 11th hour of the 11th day of the 11th month (11 am, 11 November 1918). This was the moment the guns fell silent. The first official Poppy Day was held in Britain on 11 November 1921. Invite the local British Legion to talk to the children about their role in Remembrance Day and the work they do all over the world. More information can be found at: www.britishlegion.org.uk. This activity matches the requirements of citizenship (People who help us).

> **Vocabulary:** *WWI, conflict, Armistice, ceasefire, memorial.*

Ceremony of Remembrance (page 63) outlines how some historic events are commemorated by pageantry or celebrations, which stay the same every year. Discuss with the children what happens in the local community on Remembrance Day. Watch video extracts of events in London. Point out features of the commemoration, such as wearing poppies, the uniforms and medals, the march to the Cenotaph, wreath laying, the involvement of the Queen and government representatives, two-minute silence and special music. Compare what they see on the video to events in the local community reported by the children. The activity relates to objectives in literacy (Listening and responding).

> **Vocabulary:** *Cenotaph, veteran, wreath, two-minute silence.*

Important events (page 64) helps children to understand that important events are commemorated by the wider world. Discuss why these commemorations are national and international events. Explain that on Mother's Day and Father's Day we are remembering our parents and the things they have done for us. On St Patrick's Day we are honouring the patron saint of Ireland. At Easter we remember that Jesus died on the cross. At Hogmanay we are honouring the old year and celebrating the beginning of the New Year. In small groups, the children could do a mini project, making posters or leaflets on one of the events, or one of their own ideas, and presenting them to the class. This activity meets the requirements of RE (Celebrations) and citizenship (Living in a diverse world).

> **Vocabulary:** *commemorate, Mother's Day, Father's Day, St Patrick's Day, Easter, Hogmanay.*

Finding out

Understand how historians find out about the past

- **Think of an event you have been to.**

- **Complete the chart to give information about it.**

What?	
Where?	
When?	
My picture of what happened	

- **Swap sheets with a friend.**

- **Write down what you find out about the event your friend has been to.**

Teachers' note Explain to the children that an important part of a historian's job is to select and recall information. Tell them they are going to record information about an event they have been to. Help them choose an event, such as a party. Explain they should include as many details as they can in the picture to show someone else what happened. Encourage them to write a few sentences about the event.

Developing History
Ages 6–7
© **A & C BLACK**

Evidence about me

Understand how historians find out about the past

• **Draw some pictures to tell a future historian about yourself.**

At school I like …	At home I …
At the weekend I …	I look like this …

• **Write a sentence to tell a future historian what you like to eat.**

My favourite food is _____

_____

• **Swap sheets with a friend.**
• **Write down four facts you find out about your friend.**

Teachers' note Ask the children what information they think might be interesting to a future historian. Next, brainstorm with the class some of their favourite things to do at home and school. List their ideas on the board to refer back to. Discuss how in the future historians could use the information recorded on the activity sheet to find out what life was like.

Developing History
Ages 6–7
© **A & C BLACK**

Secondary or primary?

Recognise secondary and primary sources

- ## Cut out the pictures.
- ## Sort them.

Work with a friend.

Primary	Secondary	
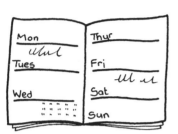 diary	 newspaper	 bone
 pottery	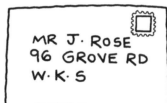 letter	 castle
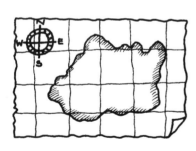 old map	 Internet	 encyclopaedia

Now try this!

- ## Write down another form of evidence historians use.

Teachers' note Use the illustrations to stimulate discussion about the different types of evidence. Explain the terms primary and secondary sources. Provide a sheet of paper for the children to glue the pictures in two sets. Encourage the children to suggest other types of evidence not shown on the activity sheet. When they have finished ask them to explain the reasons for their choices.

Developing History
Ages 6–7
© A & C BLACK

Archaeology

Find out about the past from a range of sources

What is an archaeologist **interested in?**
How does an archaeologist look for evidence?

- **Draw and label some things they might find and use as evidence.**

Archaeology is the study of the things people left behind.

e.g. bones _____
e.g jewellery _____
e.g pottery _____

Now try this!

- **What information might you find out from a skeleton?**

- **What information would you not be able to find out? Talk to a friend.**

Teachers' note Ensure children understand the difference between primary and secondary evidence. Before completing the activity sheet the children should have an opportunity to experience their own archaeological dig. Encourage the children to distinguish between what they can learn from the artefacts and what they cannot.

Developing History
Ages 6–7
© A & C BLACK

Written evidence

Find out about the past from a range of sources

• **What types of information could you find out about the past from an old newspaper?**

• **Design a front page of a newspaper reporting a school event.**

Use this idea to help you.

School
New Wildlife area opened

Now try this!

• **List three ways a modern newspaper is different from an old-fashioned one.**

Teachers' note Before completing the activity sheet, allow time for the children to examine a selection of different modern newspapers. In small groups children should list what information they contain. Do they all contain the same things? Compare these to old-fashioned newspapers.

Developing History Ages 6–7
© A & C BLACK

Photographic evidence

This photo shows three Victorian children.

Work with a friend.

What can you tell about the children from looking at the photo? _____

_____

What information can you <u>not</u> find out from the photograph? _____

_____

What other evidence could a historian use to find out more about the children? _____

_____

Now try this!

• **How are old photos different from modern ones? List your ideas.**

Teachers' note The children should work with partners to discuss their observations and complete the activity sheet. Ask them what they can see in the photo. When was the photo taken? How do they know? Can they be more precise? How old are the children? Can they be sure? What other evidence could they use to find out?

Developing History Ages 6–7
© A & C BLACK

Timeline

Place events in chronological order

Chronological means the order events happened.

- **Cut out the cards of British historical events.**
- **Add when you were born and a special event in your life.**

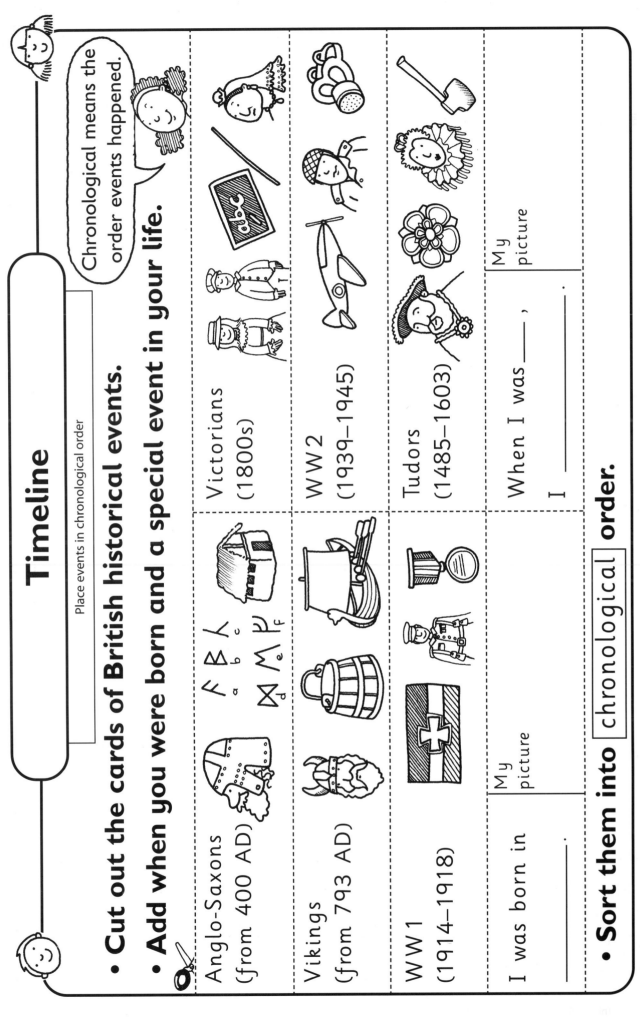

Anglo-Saxons (from 400 AD)

Vikings (from 793 AD)

WW1 (1914–1918)

I was born in ____.

| My picture |

Victorians (1800s)

WW2 (1939–1945)

Tudors (1485–1603)

When I was ____, I ____.

| My picture |

- **Sort them into** chronological **order.**

Teachers' note Photocopy onto card. Before cutting out the labels, discuss the meaning of the word 'chronological' and introduce BC and AD. Look at the dates and talk about the order they go in. The children should write in the date they were born and a significant event in their life and draw a picture on the label. Split the class into small groups and give them opportunities to decide which should come first and which should be second, etc. Attach the labels in order to a washing line with pegs. If possible provide adult support for each group.

Developing History
Ages 6–7
© A & C BLACK

Museums

- **Use this sheet to record your visit to a museum.**

I visited ...

I saw ...

The exhibits were organised by:

date ☐   item ☐

material ☐   other ☐ _____

I found out ...

This is my drawing of one of the exhibits I liked:

Was this item primary or secondary evidence?

Now try this!

- **Choose an object from the exhibition to investigate. Make notes.**
- **Report back to the class.**

Teachers' note This activity sheet could be used on a class visit to a museum or in a class museum or with an Internet museum. Talk about how the exhibits are displayed. Encourage the children to concentrate on a specific exhibit they like and do a more in-depth study of it. Provide time for the children to report back what they found out and tell the rest of the class about the exhibit they studied.

Developing History
Ages 6–7
© A & C BLACK

Holiday calendar

Explore the time of the year holidays take place

When are your school holidays ?

• Write the main school holidays in the correct places on the timeline.

September October November December January February March April May June July August

• Label what happens during these different holidays.

What are the reasons we have holidays?

• Talk to your group.

Now try this!

Teachers' note Agree with the children what holidays are and when they have holidays. Ask the children to place the three main school holidays and any other holidays they suggest on the timeline. Encourage the children to identify the relationship between holidays and religious festivals, and to think about the reasons we have holidays and what happens at different holidays.

**Developing History
Ages 6–7**
© A & C BLACK

20

Spot the mistakes

Distinguish between holidays in the recent and more distant past

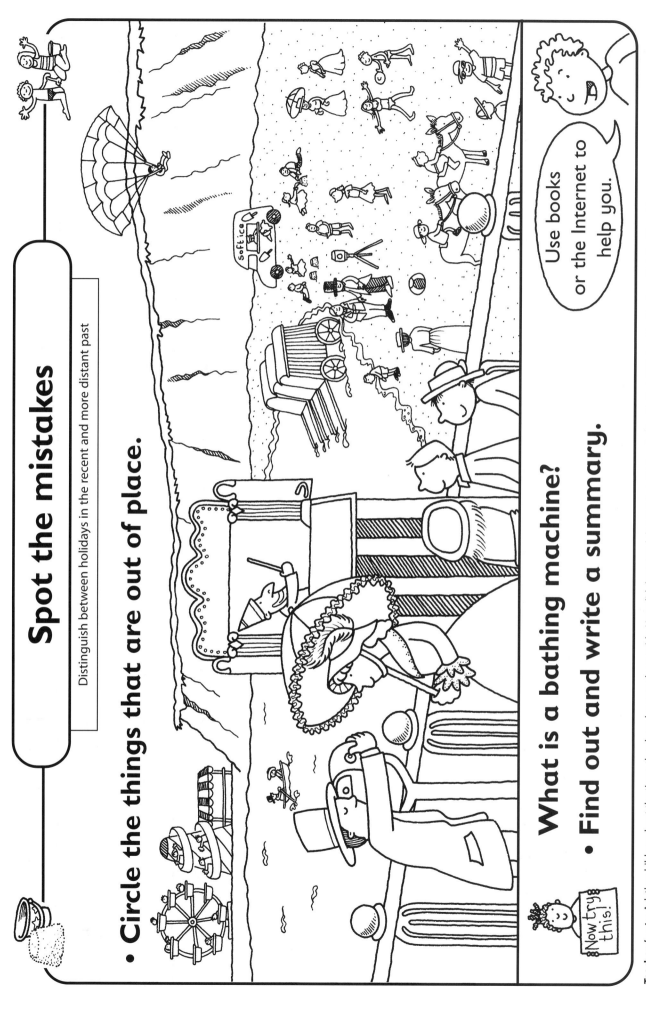

- ● **Circle the things that are out of place.**

- **What is a bathing machine?**
- ● **Find out and write a summary.**

Use books or the Internet to help you.

Developing History
Ages 6–7
© A & C BLACK

Teachers' note Ask the children about the times they have been to the seaside. How did they travel there? What did they take with them? Do they think families 100 years ago enjoyed doing the same things as they do today at the seaside? Would people have taken the same things with them on their trip to the seaside 100 years ago? Look at the Victorian scene on the sheet and discuss what you can see. What things should not be there? Ensure everyone contributes to the discussion.

Going for a swim

Sort information in chronological order

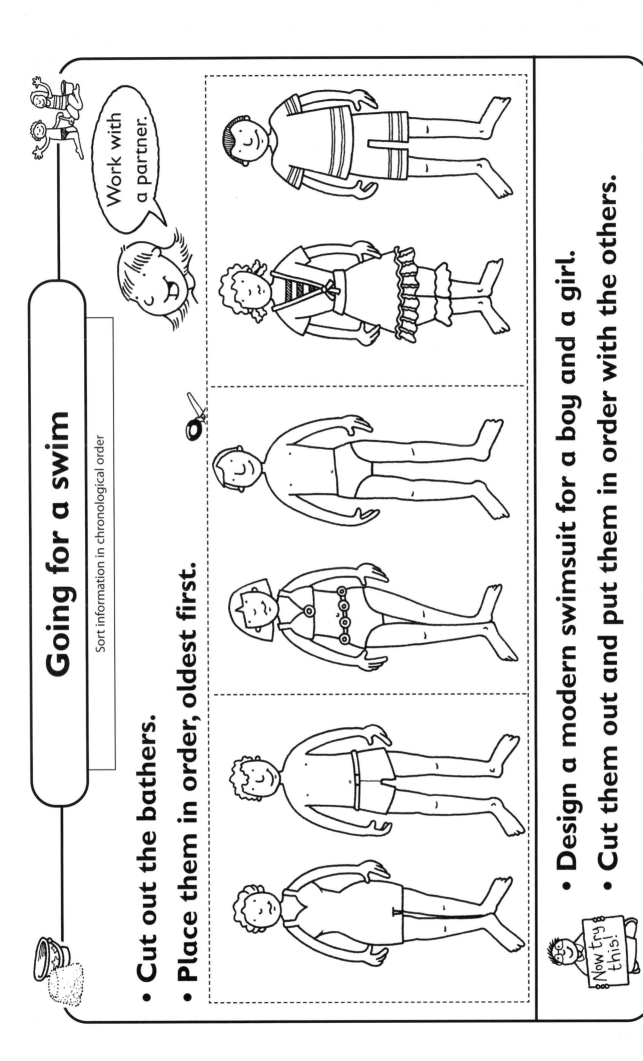

Work with a partner.

- **Cut out the bathers.**
- **Place them in order, oldest first.**

- **Design a modern swimsuit for a boy and a girl.**
- **Cut them out and put them in order with the others.**

Now try this!

Teachers' note Discuss what the people are wearing in the pictures. Which do the children think is the oldest? Why? Encourage them to give reasons for their suggestions. Identify similarities and differences between the pictures. Encourage the children to use time-related vocabulary e.g. *recent, modern, old-fashioned, older, oldest,* etc.

Developing History
Ages 6–7
© A & C BLACK

22

Holidays in the past

- **Think of three questions you would like to ask about seaside holidays in the past.**

- **Find out the answers to your questions.**

Use books and the Internet to find out.

1. _____	I found out … _____
_____	_____
_____	_____
_____	_____
2. _____	I found out … _____
_____	_____
_____	_____
_____	_____
3. _____	I found out … _____
_____	_____
_____	_____
_____	_____

Now try this!

What food can you buy at the seaside?
- **Make a list.**

Teachers' note Ask the children what they know about seaside holidays. What other things would they like to know? Brainstorm ideas and model some questions on the interactive whiteboard. Use pictures to help stimulate ideas.

Developing History
Ages 6–7
© A & C BLACK

Keepsakes

• **Draw and label a seaside holiday** souvenir .

Use your skills of observation.

What is this souvenir? _____

_____

Where did it come from? _____

_____

Why did the owner choose it? _____

_____

Now try this!

• **What do souvenirs tell us about seaside holidays in the past?**

Teachers' note This activity sheet can be used by the children to record what they observe after a visitor to the class has talked about their souvenirs. Ask the children to draw one of the souvenirs brought in by the visitor. Help them to write a caption for their pictures, explaining what information the souvenir provides about seaside holidays in the past.

Developing History
Ages 6–7
© **A & C BLACK**

Fun at the seaside

Recognise some things change while others stay the same

Sort the seaside activities into the Venn diagram.

fair

banana boat

building sandcastles

Punch and Judy

swimming pool

donkey rides

arcade games

walk along promenade

crabbing

'penny in the slot' viewing machine

portrait photography

Seaside holidays in the past

Seaside holidays today

fair

Developing History
Ages 6–7
© A & C BLACK

Teachers' note Talk about each of the activities shown on the sheet and ask if the children have had experience of them before. Where? When? Ensure all the children know what all the activities are. Encourage the children to write the captions into the Venn diagram to show whether they are activities from the past, present or both. Discuss how some things have stayed the same. Why do the children think this is so?

What makes people famous?

Identify why some people are famous

- **Draw or stick on a picture of a famous person.**

What are they famous for?

_____

_____

Where can you find more
information about this person?

_____

_____

- **Think of some more famous people and complete the chart.**

Famous people	Why they are famous
_____	_____
_____	_____
_____	_____
_____	_____

- **List all the places you can find out about famous people.**

- **How did people find out about famous people in the past? List your ideas.**

Teachers' note Have a selection of pictures of famous people all ready cut out of magazines or printed off the Internet for the children to stick onto the activity sheet, such as scientists, musicians, actors and actresses, sport celebrities, authors, chefs, politicians, etc. Brainstorm why the different people are famous before the children complete the sheet. Ask how we find out about famous people. Discuss the influence of the mass media today.

Developing History
Ages 6–7
© A & C BLACK

Wolfgang Amadeus Mozart

Investigate the life of a significant person

- **Cut out the captions and pictures. Match them.**
- **Sequence them.**

| Mozart performed to the Emperor of Austria. | Mozart began playing the piano. |
| Mozart wrote his first symphony. | Mozart became a concert master. |

Now try this!

- **What was the last piece of music Mozart composed called?**

Use books or the Internet to find out.

Teachers' note Introduce Mozart using the notes on pages 6 and 7. Discuss the pictures portraying Mozart's life. Explain that the pictures are not in the correct order and the children have to sequence them. Help them recount the story by matching the pictures to the captions and arranging them in order. Encourage the children to discuss and give reasons for their choices. Use the activity sheet to emphasise how famous Mozart was at such an early age.

Developing History
Ages 6–7
© A & C BLACK

Unbelievable talent

Recount an episode from a story from the past

Stories are a valuable source of information for historians.

Write and draw in the boxes.

- **Listen to the story.**
- **Fill in the storyboard for a short film about Mozart's life.**

- **Would you have believed such a young child was a** genius **?**

Why? _____

Now try this!

Teachers' note Enlarge this sheet onto A3 paper. Read the story from the activity notes on page 7. Point out the main events of the story. Allow time for discussion and questions. What do the children think Mozart's life was like as a child? Tell them he wanted to be a musician and enjoyed writing music. Do they think he had a good childhood? Encourage them to give reasons for their answers.

Developing History
Ages 6–7
© A & C BLACK

28

Thank you for the music

Explore achievements of a significant person

• **Listen to Mozart's music.**

What is it called?

_____

When was it composed?

_____

How is it different from pop music today?

_____

_____

• **Draw a picture to show how it makes you feel.**

Why is Mozart famous today?
• **Write a sentence.**

Teachers' note Ask the children what their favourite music, bands and singers are. Explain that Mozart was one of the top musicians of his day. Going to see Mozart perform would be like going to watch their favourite pop group today. Play the children an excerpt of a piece composed by Mozart. Does it make them feel like dancing? Singing? Humming along? Encourage the children to show how the music makes them feel by drawing pictures.

Developing History
Ages 6–7
© A & C BLACK

29

Anne Frank

• Listen to some of Anne Frank's diary.

Thursday, 9 July 1942
So there we were, Father, Mother and I, walking in the pouring rain, each of us with a satchel and a shopping bag filled to the brim with the most varied assortment of items. The people on their way to work at that early hour gave us sympathetic looks; you could tell by their faces they were sorry they couldn't offer us some kind of transport; the conspicuous yellow star spoke for itself. Where was the Secret Annex located?

Only when we were walking down the street did Father and Mother reveal, little by little, what the plan was. For months we'd been moving as much of our furniture and apparel out of the flat as we could. It was agreed that we'd go into hiding on 16 July. Because of Margot's call-up notice, the plan had been moved forward ten days, which meant we'd have to make do with less orderly rooms.

The hiding place was located in Father's office building.

Where was the secret annex located?

_____

When did the family go into hiding?

_____

Why did they go into hiding?

_____

_____

• Find out another fact about Anne Frank's life.
• Share it with a friend.

Look in Anne Frank's diary to find out more about her.

Teachers' note Read the extract to the children. Allow time for discussion and questions. Discuss in more detail what life would have been like for Anne Frank during WW2. Encourage the children to suggest adjectives that would describe Anne and her family, such as *brave, patient, determined.*

Developing History
Ages 6–7
© A & C BLACK

30

Going into hiding

Ask and answer questions about the past

• **The picture shows Anne Frank's hideout.**

Work with a friend.

What possessions did Anne have in the hideout?

Write down three things you can see in the picture.

1._____

2._____

3._____

What do you think it was like hiding in the hideout?

_____

_____

_____

Now try this!

• **Write your own diary entry about the hideout.**

• **Discuss it with a friend.**

Teachers' note Talk about the picture of the inside of the secret annex. Remind children it was in Anne's father's office building. Ask the children to tell you what they can see. Ask them what they think it would have been like to live there. Fun? Cramped? Scary? Encourage the children to suggest other adjectives that would describe what it would have been like in the secret annex.

Developing History
Ages 6–7
© A & C BLACK

Why is Anne Frank famous?

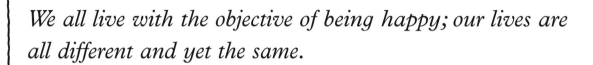

In her diary Anne Frank said:

We all live with the objective of being happy; our lives are all different and yet the same.

What do you think she meant by this?

_____

_____

Anne Frank also wrote:

In spite of everything I still believe that people are really good at heart.

What did she mean?

_____

_____

_____

Why do you think Anne Frank is famous today?

- **Tell a friend.**

Teachers' note Read the quotes and discuss their meaning with the class. List their suggestions. Encourage the children to think why Anne Frank is famous. Tell the children her diary provides important historical evidence. Emphasise how she was known for her courage and kindness because, even though such terrible things were happening around her, she was still able to write such positive things in her diary.

Developing History
Ages 6–7
© A & C BLACK

The Crimean War

Locate site of a historical event on a map

- **Look at the map.**
- **Draw on the route Florence Nightingale took to reach the Crimea.**

Use the Internet and books to find out.

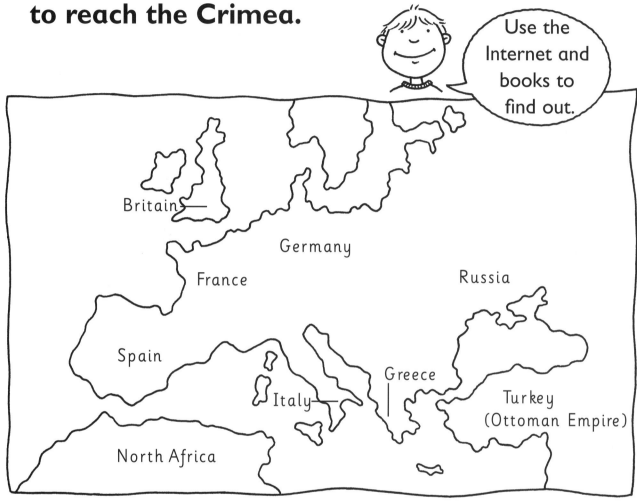

How did Florence Nightingale travel?

_____

How long did the journey take?

_____

Now try this!

- **Draw a picture of the transport Florence Nightingale used.**

Teachers' note Talk about the map and ensure the children know which parts are land and which part is the sea. Discuss how long a journey it is and how Florence Nightingale would have travelled there. Encourage children to suggest adjectives that describe people who went on long journeys by boat in those days, e.g. _brave, patient, healthy,_ etc. List their ideas to build up a class word bank.

Developing History
Ages 6–7
© **A & C BLACK**

The Charge of the Light Brigade

Infer information from a picture

• **Look at the picture and read the caption.**

Use the Internet and books to find out.

Charge of the Light Brigade (25 October 1854)

What weapons can you see?

_____

What are the British wearing on their heads?

_____

What is happening to some of the soldiers?

_____

Now try this!

What was it like to be a soldier in the Crimean War?

• **Talk to your group.**

Teachers' note Discuss the picture with the children. Ask what they can see. What do they think is happening? Tell them about the Crimean War and place the dates of the war (1854–6) on a timeline. Discuss what they think it must have been like in such a battle. Point out the weapons the soldiers are using, the different uniforms and the horses. Explain that soldiers did not have tanks and aircraft in those days.

Developing History
Ages 6–7
© A & C BLACK

The lady with the lamp

What do you think the people in the picture are saying?

- **Write a sentence in each speech bubble.**

Use the Internet and books to help you.

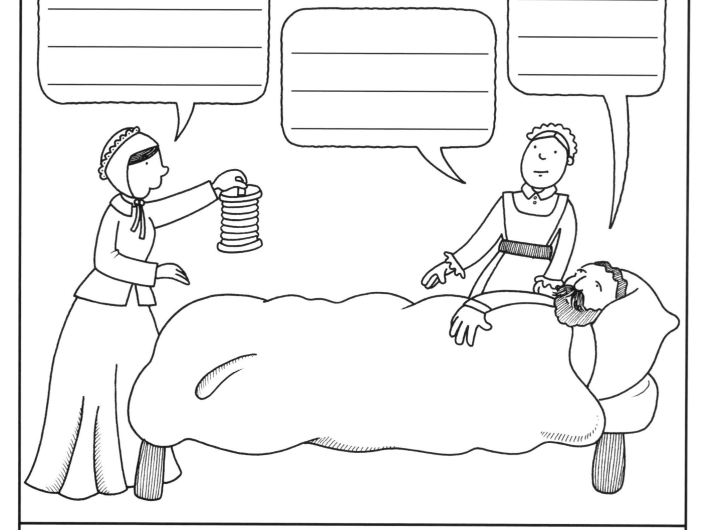

Would you like to be a patient in this hospital? Why?

- **Tell a friend.**

Teachers' note Enlarge the picture or project onto an interactive whiteboard and use to prompt class discussion. Where is Florence Nightingale? What is she wearing? What is she doing? Is it happening today or a long time ago? How can you tell she lived a long time ago? What sort of person do you think Florence Nightingale is?

Developing History
Ages 6–7
© **A & C BLACK**

Florence Nightingale's story

- ## Cut out the pictures.
- ## Put them in order.

Work with a partner.

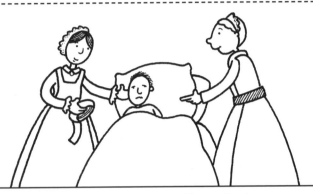

Florence eventually did train to be a nurse.

Florence's parents did not want her to be a nurse.

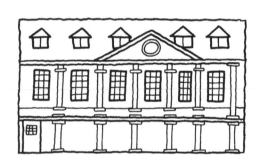

She set up a training college for nurses.

She campaigned for better conditions.

She wrote a book called 'Notes on Nursing'.

She received a letter asking her to go to Scutari.

Teachers' note First read the story of Florence Nightingale to the children (page 8). Explain the pictures are not in the correct order and the children have to sequence them. Ask them how Florence must have felt when she saw the awful conditions in the military hospital. Encourage them to use adjectives to describe her, e.g. *angry, brave, courageous, strong,* etc. List the children's ideas to produce a word bank.

36

Developing History
Ages 6–7
© A & C BLACK

An invitation

Explore why Florence Nightingale acted as she did

• **Read the letter.**

Dear Miss Nightingale,

There is a lack of nurses at the hospital of Scutari. They have plenty of medical officers as there is one to every 95 men, which is double what we have ever had before and 30 more surgeons went out three weeks ago. They also have adequate medical supplies and more are on their way.

I was hoping you would take a group of ladies who have volunteered and direct them in nursing. You would have full co-operation of the medical staff and if you need anything the government will send whatever you want. I hope you agree. Your decision will determine the success of the plan.

Would your parents give their consent to you helping out?

I know you will come to a wise decision.

> *Ever yours,*
> *Sidney Herbert, Minister at War.*

Did Florence Nightingale have to go to the Crimea?

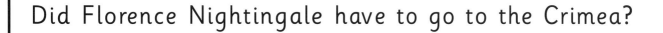

Did Florence Nightingale want to go to the Crimea?

What promises was she made?

• **Why did Florence's parents not want her to go? Write your ideas.**

Teachers' note The children should already have undertaken work on Florence Nightingale before attempting this activity sheet. Read the letter to the children. Explain what Sidney Herbert the War Minister wanted Florence Nightingale to do. Discuss the reasons why she might take up his offer. Encourage the children to refer to their previous knowledge of Florence Nightingale.

Developing History
Ages 6–7
© **A & C BLACK**

Scutari hospital

Identify features that were not hygienic

The picture shows wounded soldiers in Scutari hospital.

- Circle the things that are not hygienic .

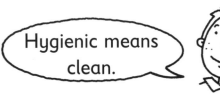

Hygienic means clean.

Now try this!

- **Find out some of Florence Nightingale's reforms.**
- **Tell a friend.**

Use books and the Internet to help you.

Teachers' note Explain that hygienic means clean and healthy. Discuss the conditions in the picture. What can the children see? Do they think this is hygienic? Why? Encourage them to complete "I can see…" statements and to use a range of adjectives to describe what it would have been like in the hospital, such as *dirty, cold, crowded,* etc. Build up a class word bank.

**Developing History
Ages 6–7**
© A & C BLACK

Remembering Florence

Investigate why Florence Nightingale is remembered today.

- **Cut out the sentences about Florence.**
- **Sort them into two groups** true **and** false .

True	False

Set up an Army Medical College.

Became a nurse because her parents wanted her to.

Opened the Nightingale Training School for Nurses.

Drank coffee all day and did no work.

Refused to treat the soldiers until the hospital was clean.

Wrote a book called 'Notes on Nursing'.

Campaigned directly to Queen Victoria for reforms, or changes.

Thought the hospital was hygienic when she arrived.

Would you like to have been a nurse in the Crimean War? Why?

- **Tell a friend.**

Teachers' note Read the sentences with the children. Ask which ones they think are true and which ones they think are false? The children should work together in small groups to sort the cards into two sets. They should take turns to pick a card and place it in a set. The whole group must agree which set each card belongs before they tick the box to show true or false. Ask them to explain their decision. If the other children disagree encourage them to explain why.

Developing History
Ages 6–7
© **A & C BLACK**

Mary Seacole

Sequence main events

- **Listen to the story.**
- **Match the captions to the pictures.**
- **Put the pictures in order.**

Cut out the pictures and the captions.

Mary Seacole cared for yellow-fever victims	She volunteered to go to the Crimea
She set up the British Hotel, which had recovery wards.	Celebrations were held in London in her honour

Teachers' note Read the sentences with the children. Discuss this true story before the children attempt ordering the sentences themselves. When they have finished ordering the sentences and pictures, ask why they decided to put them in the order they have.

Developing History Ages 6–7 © A & C BLACK

40

Mary Seacole's story

Explore why Mary Seacole acted as she did

- ## Cut out the cards.
- ## Use them for role-play activities about Mary Seacole's life.

Work in a group.

Mary Seacole

War Minister, Sydney Herbert

doctor

nurse

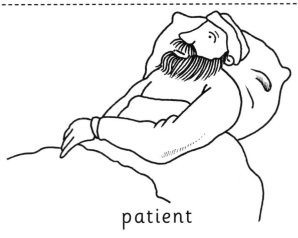

patient

patient

Teachers' note One copy is needed for each group. Discuss why Mary Seacole wanted to be a nurse. Why do they think she was told she was not needed in the Crimea? Mary believed it was because of the colour of her skin. Do they think this was fair? Why? In pairs, discuss what they would do if someone would not let them do something for an unfair reason. Do they think it was the right decision to go to the Crimea and set up her own hospital?

Developing History
Ages 6–7
© A & C BLACK

Newsflash

- **Write your own news report about the celebrations for Mary Seacole.**

THE TIMES

31 July 1857

Mary Seacole Honoured

_____

_____

_____

_____

_____

_____

_____

_____

_____

_____

_____

_____

_____

_____

- **Share your report with a partner.**

Now try this!

Teachers' note Tell the children about the celebrations held in London in honour of Mary Seacole in 1857. Information can be found on website www.maryseacole.com. Encourage the children to write and draw in the columns to produce their own newspaper report on the event. Suggest they add pictures. Point out the date of the newspaper. Explain they are reporting the event as if it were the day after it happened. Less able children will need more adult support.

Developing History
Ages 6–7
© **A & C BLACK**

Compare and contrast

Compare lives of two famous people

- **Compare the lives of Mary Seacole and Florence Nightingale.**
- **Complete the chart.**

Use books and the Internet to help you.

	Florence Nightingale	Mary Seacole
Draw their portraits here.		
What did they do before they went to the Crimea?		
What did they do in the Crimea?		
What did they do after the Crimean War?		

Teachers' note Ask the children what they remember about Florence Nightingale and Mary Seacole. List their ideas on the board. Talk about both women's lives before and after the Crimean War. How were they similar? How were they different? How did they help? Encourage the children to use adjectives to describe both women to add to the class word bank.

Developing History
Ages 6–7
© **A & C BLACK**

43

The Monument

- **Draw the Monument.**
- **Label the details.**

Use books and the Internet to help you.

Top	
Middle	
Base	

Now try this!

- **Find out where the Monument is.**

Use maps to help you.

Teachers' note Use pictures, books and the Internet for children to get a good idea of what the Monument looks like to sketch on the activity sheet and to add labels and perhaps a background. The following website provides a good view of the Monument: www.Victorianweb.org/art/architecture/feist/31.html. Encourage them to use their observation skills. Identify where the Monument is, when it was built and what it commemorates.

**Developing History
Ages 6–7
© A & C BLACK**

Portrait gallery

Identify differences between ways of life at different times

• What can you tell about these people from their portraits?

Charles II	_____ _____ _____ _____
Samuel Pepys	_____ _____ _____ _____
Christopher Wren	_____ _____ _____ _____

• How do they look different from men today?

_____

_____

_____

Now try this!

Where would you place them on a timeline?
• Show a friend.

Teachers' note Introduce the three men in the pictures. Tell the children briefly about their lives and how they are connected to the Great Fire of London. Ask the children to describe the hairstyles and the appearance of each of the three men. Note that all have wigs and neckerchiefs, and none have a beard or moustache. Does the king look the most important and if so, how? Does Samuel Pepys look like a rich or poor person? Why do the children think this is?

Developing History
Ages 6–7
© A & C BLACK

Fire! Fire!

- ## Cut out the pictures of the Great Fire of 1666.
- ## Put the pictures in order.

Now try this!

- ## Imagine you were in the fire. Use your senses to describe what it was like.

Complete the sentences.

I can see ...	I can hear ...

I can smell ...	I can feel ...	I can taste ...

Teachers' note Introduce the activity sheet by singing the rhyme *London's Burning* and explain they are going to learn about the Great Fire of London. Discuss what is happening in each of the pictures. Point out important features the children can see. Ask what the houses are made from. Arrange the pictures on a timeline. Encourage the children to talk about their own experiences of bonfires; ask them what did they smell, taste, etc. List their ideas.

**Developing History
Ages 6–7
© A & C BLACK**

When? Where? Why?

- **Cut out and match the sentences and** explanations **.**

Work with a partner.

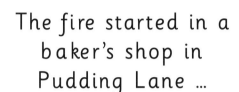

Sentences	Explanations
The fire started in a baker's shop in Pudding Lane …	… because the churches were made of stone and people believed they would not burn.
The fire spread very quickly …	… because they believed they would be safe in the water.
Some people ran to the churches …	… because the ovens were not put out properly.
Some people ran to the river …	… because the wind stopped, people created fire breaks by pulling down houses and more people came to help.
The fire eventually stopped after four days …	… because it was a windy night, the houses were made of wood and it had not rained for a long time.

Now try this!

- **Find out which buildings were destroyed.**

Use books and the Internet to help you.

Teachers' note Show the children pictures of typical 17th-century houses, churches and street scenes. Encourage them to describe the street scene and what the houses are made from. Read the sentences and explanations with the children. Discuss what is meant by 'explanation'. Working with a partner the children should match each sentence with an explanation. During the plenary, ask them to explain how they knew which belonged together.

Developing History
Ages 6–7
© A & C BLACK

London's burning

• **Look at the picture of the Great Fire of London.**

Give two | reasons | why the fire spread so quickly.

_____

_____

Name two places people ran to safety.

_____

_____

Give two reasons the fire stopped.

_____

_____

• **Why is it called the Great Fire of London? Write a sentence.**

Teachers' note Remind children of what they learned about the Great Fire from pages 46 and 47. Talk about what they can see in the picture. Use the activity notes at the front of the book to stimulate discussion. Ask questions to check their understanding. Why did the fire start? Where did it start? What happened? Why did it end? What were the results of the fire? Use a map of London to plot the progress of the fire.

48

**Developing History
Ages 6–7**
© A & C BLACK

Samuel Pepys' diary

- **This cartoon strip is based on Samuel Pepys'** diary .

What a sad sight it was to see the whole City on fire.

I rode down to the waterside, and there saw a lamentable fire.

His Majesty did command houses to be pulled down.

- **Write your own diary entry about the Great Fire of London.**

2 September 1666

_____

_____

_____

_____

_____

_____

_____

Teachers' note Read the abridged extracts from Samuel Pepys' diary. Ensure the children understand what is happening. Explain they are going to write their own diary extract about what it might have been like in the Great Fire. Brainstorm describing words and list them for the children to use in their writing. Encourage them to read their entries to the class. Discuss the similarities and differences between them.

Developing History
Ages 6–7
© **A & C BLACK**

49

Sir Christopher Wren

Sir Christopher Wren was a famous architect **.**

- **Label Christopher Wren's designs.**

Use books and the Internet to help you.

Word bank
The Monument
Royal Observatory
St Paul's Cathedral
Kensington Palace
Trinity College Library
St Bride's Steeple
Royal Hospital

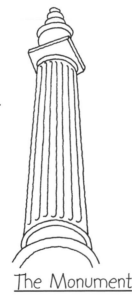

The Monument

Now try this!

- **Find the buildings on a map of London.**
- **Find out why people think these buildings are important.**

Work with a partner.

Teachers' note Emphasise the wide variety of Sir Christopher Wren's achievements and designs. Ask if any of the children have seen or been to any of these buildings. Ask the children to find and write down some important facts about these buildings using books and the Internet. The picture are: Kensington Palace top left; St Bride's top middle; Hospital top right; St Paul's centre left; Observatory bottom left, Monument bottom centre; Trinity College bottom right.

Developing History
Ages 6–7
© **A & C BLACK**

St Paul's Cathedral

Discover how the cathedral has changed over time

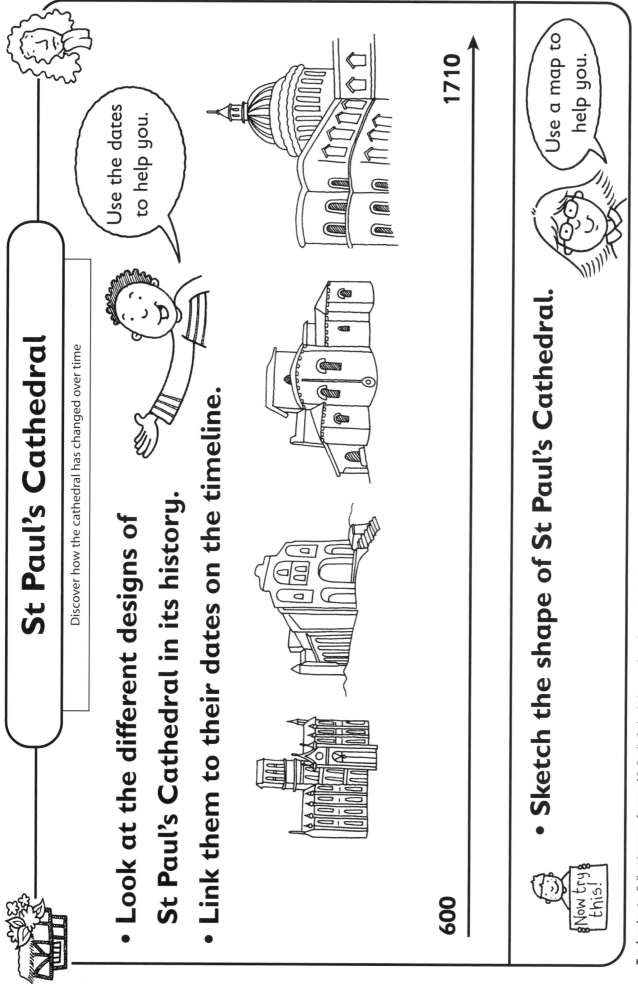

- Look at the different designs of St Paul's Cathedral in its history.
- Link them to their dates on the timeline.

Use the dates to help you.

600 ———————————→ 1710

- **Sketch the shape of St Paul's Cathedral.**

Use a map to help you.

Now try this!

Teachers' note Collect images of parts of St Paul's Cathedral to use for reference in the classroom. Look at its shape, pattern and decoration. Tell the children the cathedral had to be rebuilt several times in its history. Look at the dates and discuss whereabouts the four pictures should be placed on the timeline. Ask the children to estimate where on the timeline they should be placed. Discuss the differences in appearance. Explain how long it took to build each time. Point out how St Paul's has become larger and more elaborate. Mark the Great Fire on the timeline.

Developing History
Ages 6–7
© A & C BLACK

The fire brigade

Gain an understanding of the tools available in 1666

- **Cut out the pictures.**
- **Sort them.**

Work with a friend.

1666	1966	
 leather bucket	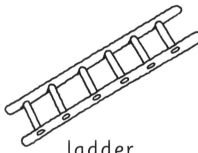 ladder	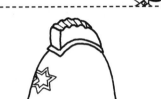 helmet
 water-pump	 hook	 fire-extinguisher
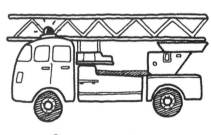 fire-engine	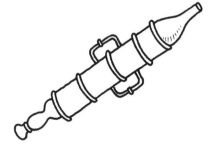 hand-squirt	 hosepipe

Now try this!

- **Make a fire safety poster for people in 1666.**

Teachers' note Tell the children there was no fire brigade in 1666 and straight after 1666 things did not improve much. It took nearly 300 years before a proper fire service was introduced. Provide a sheet of paper for the children to glue the pictures in two sets. Encourage the children to suggest other types of firefighting equipment not shown on the activity sheet, such as uniforms and safety masks. When they have finished ask them to explain the reason for their choices.

Developing History
Ages 6–7
© **A & C BLACK**

How do we know?

Find out about the past from artefacts

We know a lot about the ancient Greeks from their pottery **.**

• **Design your own Greek pot showing the first ever Olympic event.**

Use pictures, books and the Internet to help you.

Why did the Ancient Greeks hold games?

• **Write a sentence.**

Teachers' note Tell the children we know a lot about the ancient Greeks from their pottery. Show examples of ancient Greek pots and encourage them to draw a design on the pot in the style of the ancient Greeks. Display their designs. Tell the children the first recorded Olympic Games were in 776 BC. However, the games probably started about 500 years before this. The first event was running a stade (192 m). This is where the word 'stadium' comes from.

Developing History
Ages 6–7
© **A & C BLACK**

Olympic events

Explore past events

- **Look at these pictures of the Olympic Games.**

- **Name the different sports.**

Use the word bank to help you.

Word bank

boxing
chariot racing
horse racing
long jump
javelin

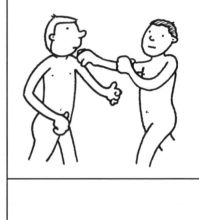

- **What other sports are held at the Olympic Games today? Make a list.**

Teachers' note Tell the children we know a lot about the ancient Greeks from their pottery. Show examples of ancient Greek pots and the types of designs on them. Talk about the variety of sports held in the ancient games and compare them to the Olympic Games today. Which ones are the same? Which ones are different?

Developing History
Ages 6–7
© A & C BLACK

Ancient Olympia

Find out about past events by studying their location

In Olympia, buildings were designed for different sports.

- **Find out which events occurred in each of these buildings. Use the Internet to help you.**

Some areas had more than one event.

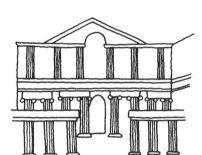

gymnasium

hippodrome

Word bank
award ceremony
boxing
chariot racing
discus
horse racing
javelin
jumping
running
wrestling

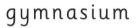

stadium

Temple of Zeus

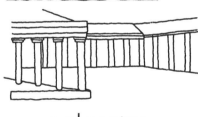

palaestra

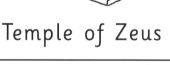

- **Find Olympia on a map.**

Teachers' note Read the words in the word bank and ensure the children understand what each event is. They will need access to Internet for the main activity and to maps for the extension activity. Tell them the Olympic Games were first held at Olympia in Greece and were held there every four years in honour of the ancient Greek god Zeus. In which area do they think the events were held? Afterwards, discuss their answers as a class.

Athletic events

Investigate features associated with the Olympic Games

- **Look at the sports in the modern decathlon .**

| 100 m | long jump | shot put | high jump | 400 m |
| 110 m hurdles | discus | pole vault | javelin | 1500 m |

- **Circle any sports in the modern heptathlon .**
- **List any you cannot see.**

_____

_____

Use a different colour pencil.

- **Circle the ones in the ancient pentathlon .**
- **List any you cannot see.**

_____

_____

Use books and the Internet to help you.

- **What sports are in the triathlon ?**

_____

_____

Now try this!

- **Find out how the marathon got its name.**
- **Tell a friend.**

Teachers' note Ensure the children understand what all the events shown on the activity sheet are. Discuss the four different competitions – triathlon, pentathlon, heptathlon and decathlon and explain how they got their names from Greek numbers 3, 5, 7 and 10. Explain how many events they are looking for in each one. It is also important to point out the similarities and differences between the male and female versions of the competitions.

**Developing History
Ages 6–7
© A & C BLACK**

Ancient and modern

Identify differences between ways of life at different times

- **Cut out the cards.**
- **Sort them.**

Work in a group.

Ancient	Modern	Both
Running		Relay
Wrestling		Discus
Javelin		Pentathlon
Winners are heroes		No money prizes
Athletes spend years training		Chariot races
Armour races		Only men take part
Win olive leaf crowns		Athletes are naked
Rowing		Swimming
Horse jumping		Win medals
Shown on television		Men and women take part

Now try this!

- **List some of the places the Olympic Games have been held.**
- **Find these places on a map or globe.**

Teachers' note One activity sheet is needed for each group. The children should take turns to pick a card and place it in one of the sets – Ancient, Modern or Both. The whole group must try to agree which set each card belongs to. Ask them to explain their decision. If the other children disagree, encourage them to explain why. The children will need access to maps or globes for the extension activity.

**Developing History
Ages 6–7
© A & C BLACK**

Olympic traditions

These pictures show some Olympic traditions.

- ## Write a sentence about each of the pictures.

Use books and the Internet to help you.

Teachers' note First, discuss all these pictures with the children, with reference to the notes on page 11. Ask the children why there are lots of flags from different countries around the stadium. What do the Olympic rings symbolise? Why is there a carnival parade? Why are the athletes walking around the stadium? Where does the Olympic torch start from? What do the doves symbolise? Provide time for the children to find out the answers in books and on the Internet.

Developing History
Ages 6–7
© A & C BLACK

58

Anniversaries

Understand symbols represent commemorative events

Symbol	Event	Date celebrated	Who remembering?

- **Write about another anniversary.**

Teachers' note Talk about the symbols and what they remind the children of. Why do they remind the children of these events? Can they think of any other symbols that would remind them of these events? Ensure they know when these events are celebrated. Tell them they happen every year. Can they think of any other anniversaries? Make a class list.

Developing History
Ages 6–7
© A & C BLACK

War memorial

Use local historical sources to find information

- **Sketch your local** | war memorial |.

Look very carefully and draw what you see.

Which war did the soldiers we are | commemorating | die in?_____

Tally the names._____
List any surnames that appear more than once.

_____

_____

_____

Who built the war memorial?

- **Find out.**

Teachers' note This activity sheet is to use on a trip to visit the local war memorial. Discuss war memorials and why they were built. Explain they are to remind us of all the soldiers who died in wars. Encourage the children to describe and draw accurately what they can see. Point out the lists of names, dates and symbols. Discuss how people with the same surname may be related to each other and identify families who lost more than one person.

Developing History
Ages 6–7
© **A & C BLACK**

Remembrance Day fact file

Understand poppies are worn as a symbol of Remembrance Day

Poppies are sold on Remembrance Day.

- **Find out about Remembrance Day and answer the questions.**

What date is Remembrance Day?

_____

_____

_____

What are we remembering?

_____

_____

_____

Why was a poppy chosen as a symbol?

_____

_____

_____

What other things happen on Remembrance Day?

_____

_____

_____

Now try this!

- **What other symbols are worn to commemorate things? Make a list.**

Teachers' note Explain the origins of Remembrance Day lie in World War I (1914–18). Talk about how the soldiers died protecting the UK from invasion. Mark the dates of the world wars on a timeline. Emphasise that we remember people who died in other wars as well. Talk about why the poppy was chosen as a symbol. Discuss saint days and how plants such as daffodils, shamrocks, etc. are worn as symbols on these days.

Developing History
Ages 6–7
© A & C BLACK

Armistice

- ## Cut out and match the captions and pictures.

| Soldiers from many countries fought in World War I. | Today, plastic poppies are sold to raise money for veterans. |
| Soldiers saw poppies growing in the battlefields. | The soldiers fought from trenches dug in the fields. |

Now try this!

- ## Find out more about the British Legion.
- ## Tell a friend what you find out.

Use books and the Internet to help you.

Teachers' note Discuss the Armistice with the children using the pictures and captions as prompts. Explain that the captions are not in the correct order and they have to match them to the pictures. Afterwards, discuss the role of the British Legion and their role in selling the poppies.

62

Developing History
Ages 6–7
© A & C BLACK

Ceremony of Remembrance

Recognise some historic events are commemorated by pageantry

- **The picture shows the main event of Remembrance Day in London.**

- **Label it. Use the word bank.**

Word bank

poppy
wreath
Queen Elizabeth II
Cenotaph
veterans
uniform
medals

Now try this!

- **Compare this with your local remembrance service. Write a sentence about how yours is different.**

_____

_____

_____

Teachers' note Talk about the picture and what it shows. Read the word bank to the children. Ensure they understand everything that is listed. Discuss and compare local parades and the celebrations in London. Tell the children to find the words listed in the picture and label them.

Developing History
Ages 6–7
© A & C BLACK

Important events

- ## What do these events commemorate?

Mother's Day

_____

_____

_____

_____

Write in the boxes.

Easter

_____

_____

_____

_____

Father's Day

_____

_____

_____

_____

Hogmanay

_____

_____

_____

_____

St Patrick's Day

_____

_____

_____

_____

Now try this!

- ## Find out about another event that people commemorate.
- ## Tell a friend what it commemorates and why.

Teachers' note Brainstorm other events that we commemorate and make a list. Ask the children what dates they are celebrated. Are they commemorated all over the world? When? Why? How? Identify similarities and differences between Remembrance Day and these other events that are commemorated.

Developing History
Ages 6–7
© A & C BLACK